101 Pop Hits Busker

Piano/Organ Edition with Guitar Chords.

Wise Publications
London/New York/Sydney/Cologne

Exclusive Distributors:
Music Sales Limited
8/9 Frith Street, London W1V 5TZ, England.
Music Sales Pty. Limited
120 Rothschild Avenue, Rosebery, NSW 2018, Australia.

This book © Copyright 1986 by
Wise Publications
ISBN 0.7119.0814.1
Order No. AM61763

Design & Art Direction by Mike Bell.
Cover illustration by Alistair Graham.
Arranged by Peter Lavender
Compiled by Peter Lavender & Peter Evans.
Processed by Hillmob Music Services.

Music Sales complete catalogue lists thousands of
titles and is free from your local music book shop,
or direct from Music Sales Limited.
Please send £1 in stamps for postage to
Music Sales Limited, 8/9 Frith Street, London W1V 5TZ, England.

Printed and bound in Great Britain by
Anchor Press Limited, Tiptree, Essex.

1
Against All Odds
(Take A Look At Me Now)

Words & Music by Phil Collins

Slow rock ♩ = 56

1. How can I just let you walk a-way, just let you leave with-out a trace? When I
(2, 3. see additional lyrics)

stand here tak - ing ev - 'ry breath with you;___ Ooh,_____ You're the

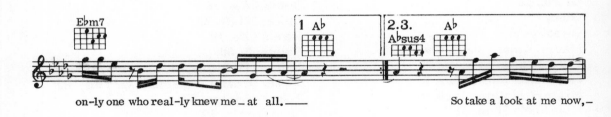

on-ly one who real-ly knew me at all. ___ So take a look at me now, ―

___ Well there's just an emp-ty space, ___ And there's nothing

left here to remind___ me, just the mem - 'ry of___ your face, ― Well take a look at me now. ―

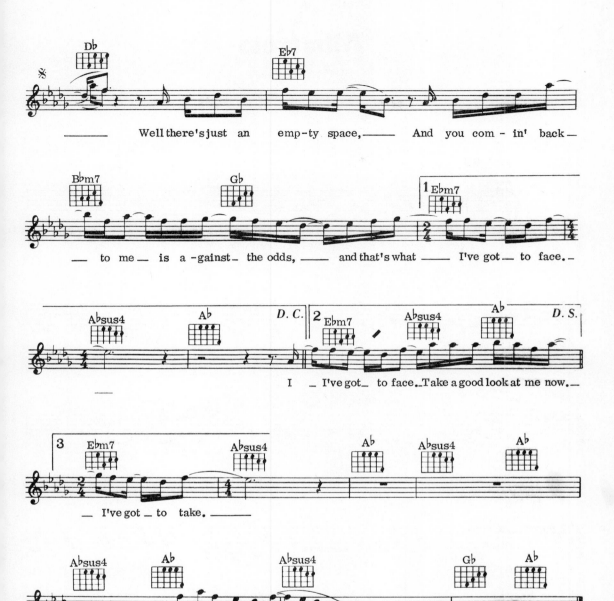

Well there's just an emp-ty space,——— And you com - in' back ——
—— to me —— is a -gainst— the odds, —— and that's what —— I've got — to face. —
I —— I've got— to face.—Take a good look at me now.—
—— I've got — to take. ———
Take a look at me now. ————

2. How can you just walk away from me
When all I can do is watch you leave?
'Cause we shared the laughter and the pain,
And even shared the tears.
You're the only one who really knew me at all.

3. I wish I could just make you turn around,
Turn around and see me cry.
There's so much I need to say to you,
So many reasons why.
You're the only one who really knew me at all.

2
Albatross

By Peter A. Green

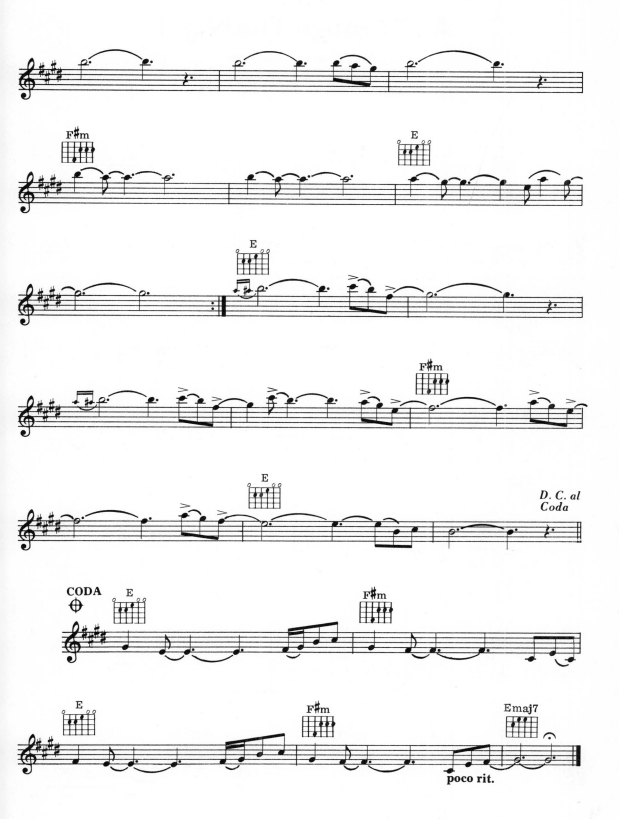

3
All Through The Night

Words & Music by James Shear

4
Angela
(Theme from 'Taxi')

By Bob James

5
A Rockin' Good Way
(To Mess Around and Fall In Love)

Words & Music by
Brook Benton, Luchi de Jesus & Clyde Otis

6
Atmosphere

Words & Music by
E. Tucker, B. Findon & S. Rodway

Moderato

Oh what an at-mos-phere I love a par-ty with a hap-py at-mos-phere

so let me take you there and you and I'll be danc-in' in the cool night air.

Well we're at a danc-ing par-ty and you're
out here all to-geth-er ev-'ry

out there hav-ing fun and your girl is there be-side
bod-y's hand in hand, we can make it last for-ev-

you and you feel like numb-er one. So
-er when we're danc-in' with the gang. Well you've

get your bod-y mov-ing 'cause to-night has just be-gun
got your fav-'rite rec-ords and Fran-kie's got his banned

(Oh!) Oh _____ let it go, oh _____ let it show,

Ah _____ Oh what an at - mos - phere I

love a par - ty with a hap-py at - mos - phere, so let me take _ you there _ and

you and I'll _ be danc-ing in the cool night _ air. _____ Oh what an at - mos - phere _ I

love a par - ty with a hap-py at - mos - phere _ mu - sic ev - 'ry - where _ and

soon we'll be danc-in' in the cool night _ air. _____ Now we're _____ Oh what an

7
All Cried Out

Words & Music by
Tony Swain, Steve Jolley, Alison Moyet

I — — I —

Gm

I'm all cried

out, you took a whole lot of lov-in' for one hand-ful of no-thing.

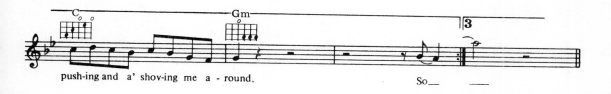

Gm   B♭

All cried out, it's hard to give you some-thing when you're

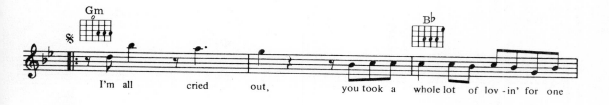

C   Gm   3

push-ing and a' shov-ing me a - round. So __ __

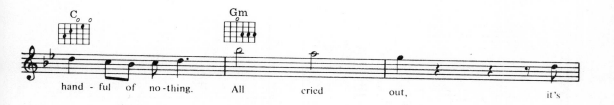

Gm   B♭

I'm all cried out, you took a whole lot of lov - in' for one

C   Gm

hand - ful of no -thing. All cried out, it's

hard to give you some-thing when you're pushing and a' shov-ing   push-ing and a' shov-ing me a-

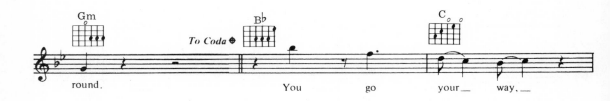

round.   You   go   your __ way, __

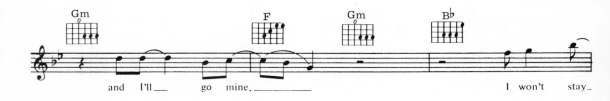

and I'll __ go mine, _____   I won't   stay __

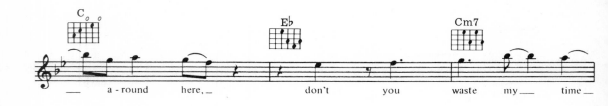

__ a-round   here, __   don't   you   waste   my __ time __

I'm all   cried

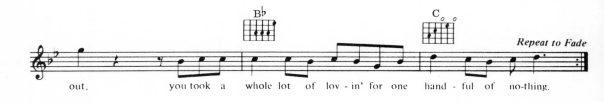

out,   you took a   whole lot   of lov-in' for one   hand-ful of no-thing.

8
Backfield In Motion

Words & Music by
Herbert T. McPherson & Melvin Harden

9
California Dreaming

Words & Music by John Phillips

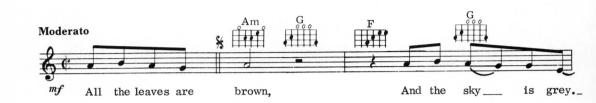

Moderato

mf

All the leaves are brown, And the sky __ is grey. __

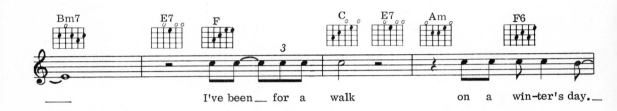

__ I've been __ for a walk on a win-ter's day. __

1. I'd be safe and warm, __
2. If I did – n't tell her, __

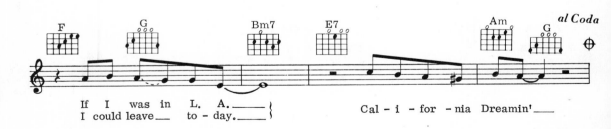

al Coda

If I was in L. A. __
I could leave __ to - day. __

Cal - i - for - nia Dreamin' __

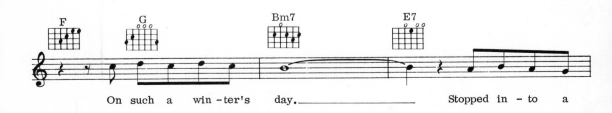

On such a win-ter's day. __ Stopped in - to a

10
Call Me

Words & Music by Peter Cox & Richard Drummie

Em

vic - tim   of a hit___ and run,___   won't   you___ }
is the pow - er of___ the press,___   will   you___ }
please id - en - ti - fy___ your - self_

Cmaj7

CHORUS

call   me   call   me,_____

D/E

no   time   to hes - i - tate._____   We

Cmaj7

must com-mun - ic - ate; _____   call   me,

Am7   G

call   me,_____   won't   you_ call   this

C   D

num - ber   now._____

3   *D.S. Repeat chorus to fade*

Caribbean Queen
(No More Love On The Run)

Words & Music by Keith Diamond & Billy Ocean

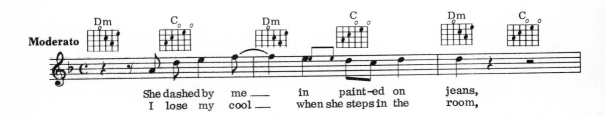

She dashed by me ___ in paint-ed on jeans,
I lose my cool ___ when she steps in the room,

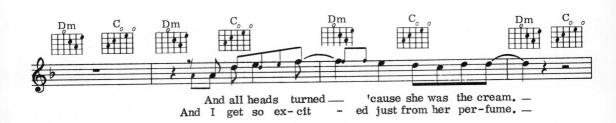

And all heads turned ___ 'cause she was the cream. ___
And I get so ex-cit - ed just from her per-fume. ___

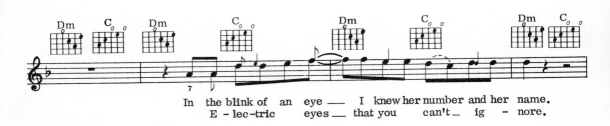

In the blink of an eye ___ I knew her number and her name.
E - lec-tric eyes ___ that you can't ___ ig - nore.

She said I was the ti - ger I want-ed to tame. ___
and pas - sion burns you like ne - ver be - fore. ___

Car-ib-be-an Queen, Now we're shar - ing the same dream, ___

12
Come Back And Stay

Words & Music by Jack Lee

Moderato

mf Since you've been gone,_____ bye.

I shut my eyes__
I was trying to hide
op - ened my

____ and I fan - ta - size_____ that you're here with me,_____
____ what I felt in - side un - til it passed me by_____
eyes and I re - al - ised what we had to - geth - er_____

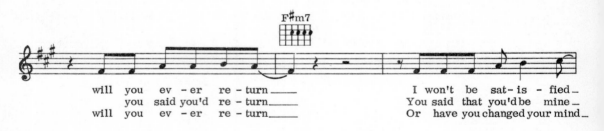

will you ev - er re - turn_____ I won't be sat - is - fied
you said you'd re - turn_____ You said that you'd be mine
will you ev - er re - turn_____ Or have you changed your mind__

al Coda ⊕

____ 'til you're by my side.____ Don't wait an - y long - er.____
____ 'til the end of time, well don't__ wait an - y long - er.____
if you wan - na stay mine,____ just love me for - ev - er.____

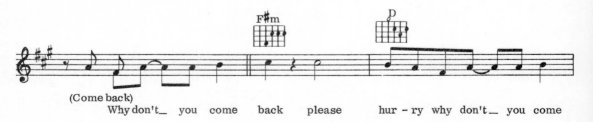

(Come back)
Why don't__ you come back please hur - ry why don't__ you come

13
Crocodile Rock

Words & Music by
Elton John & Bernie Taupin

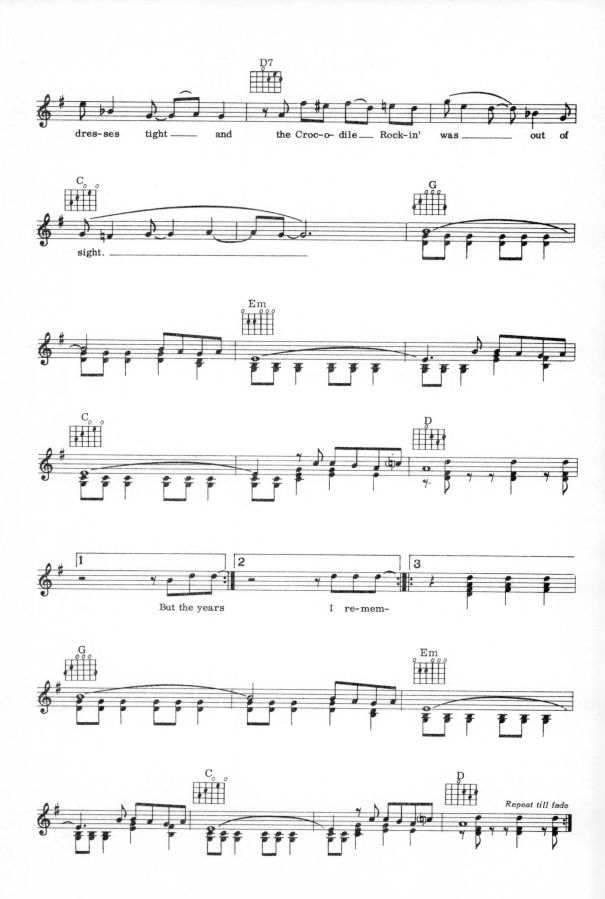

14
Dancing In The Dark

Words & Music by Bruce Springsteen

_____ with-out_ a spark._____ This gun's for hire_____
_____ o-ver a bro-ken heart._____ This gun's for hire_____

To Coda

e-ven if we're just danc - ing in_____ the dark._____

1. D.S. 2.

You sit a-round get-ting old - er; there's a joke _ here some-where,_

_____ and it's_ on me. I'll shake this world off my shoul - ders.

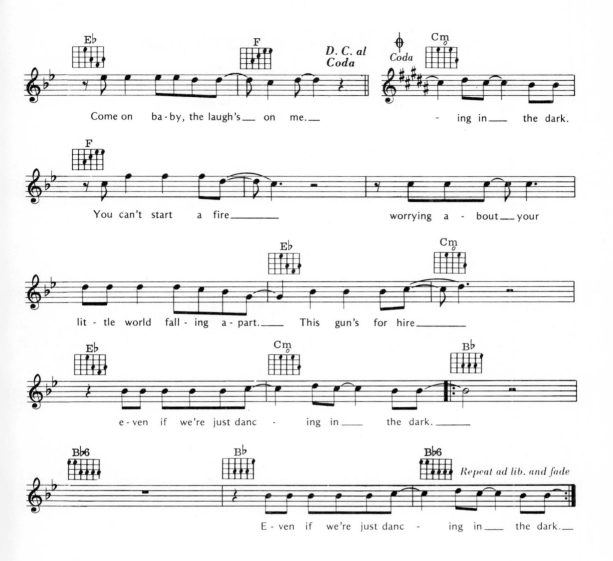

Verse 2:
Message keeps getting clearer;
Radio's on and I'm moving 'round the place.
I check my look in the mirror;
I wanna change my clothes, my hair, my face.
Man, I ain't getting nowhere just living in a dump like this.
There's something happening somewhere;
Baby I just know there is.

(To Chorus:)

Verse 3:
Stay on the streets of this town
And they'll be carving you up all right.
They say you got to stay hungry;
Hey baby I'm just about starving tonight.
I'm dying for some action;
I'm sick of sitting 'round here trying to write this book.
I need a love reaction;
Come on now baby gimme just one look.

(To Chorus:)

15
Don't Pay The Ferryman

Words & Music by Chris de Burgh

Moderato

1. It was late at night on the op-en road.___ Speed-ing like a man on the run___
Roam-ing mist___ then he gets on board,___ now there'-ll be no turn-ing back.___

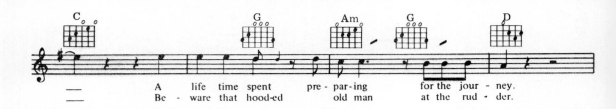

___ A life time spent pre-par-ing for the jour - ney.
___ Be - ware that hood-ed old man at the rud - der.

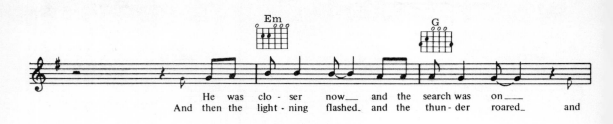

He was clo - ser now___ and the search was on___
And then the light-ning flashed___ and the thun-der roared___ and

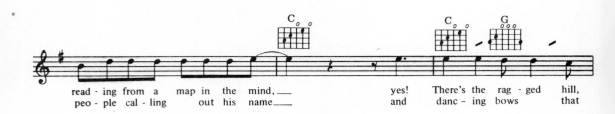

read - ing from a map in the mind, ___ yes! There's the rag-ged hill, that
peo - ple cal - ling out his name___ and danc - ing bows that

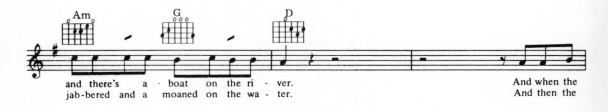

and there's a boat on the ri - ver. And when the
jab - bered and a moaned on the wa - ter. And then the

16
Don't Stand So Close To Me

Words & Music by Sting

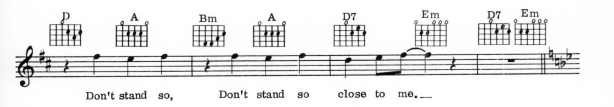

Don't stand so,   Don't stand so   close to me. ___

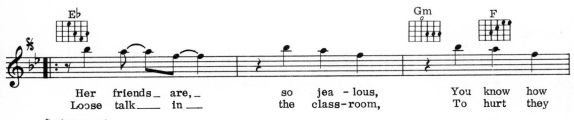

𝄋 = Instrumental

Her friends_ are,_   so jea - lous,   You know how
Loose talk___ in ___   the class-room,   To hurt they

bad girls__ get._   Some-times it's not so ea - sy,   To be the
try and ___ try._   Strong words in the staff-room, The ac - cu -

tea - cher's___ pet. _   Temp - ta - tion,   Frus - tra - tion,
sa - tions___ fly._   It's no use,   He sees her,

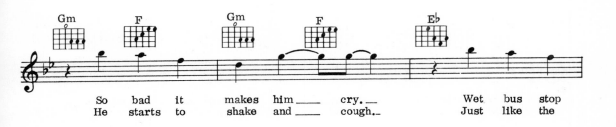

So bad it makes him ___ cry. _   Wet bus stop
He starts to shake and ___ cough._   Just like the

She's wait - ing,   His car is   warm and____ dry.__
old man in   that book by   Nab - a - kov.__

CHORUS

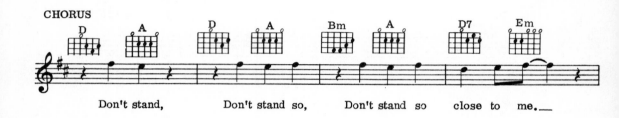

Don't stand,   Don't stand so,   Don't stand so close to me.__

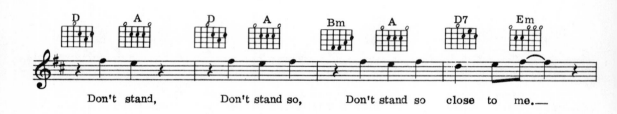

Don't stand,   Don't stand so,   Don't stand so close to me.__

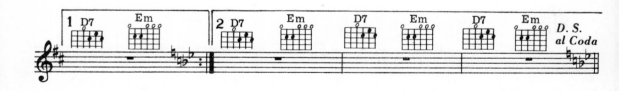

CODA

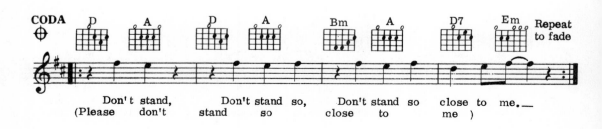

Don't stand,   Don't stand so,   Don't stand so close to me.__
(Please don't   stand   so   close to   me)

17
Do The Conga

Words & Music by Mick Flinn & Peter Morris

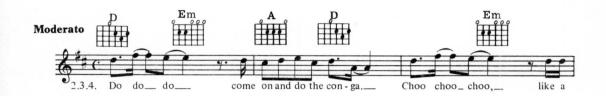

Moderato

2.3.4. Do do__ do__ come on and do the con - ga.__ Choo choo_ choo,__ like a

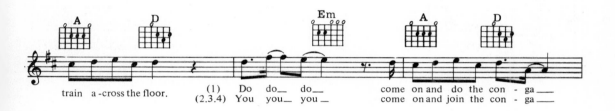

train a -cross the floor. (1) Do do__ do__ come on and do the con - ga __
(2.3.4) You you__ you __ come on and join the con - ga __

1.2.

do do__ do__ it's con - ga night for sure. It's con - ga,__ it's con - ga night,__ so
do do__ do__ it's con - ga night for sure. It's con - ga,__ it's con - ga night,__ so

join the par - ty ev -'ry - one, the danc-ing's just be - gun, and we're all hav-ing
feel the mu - sic and the beat, they're danc-ing in the street, it's some-thing that I

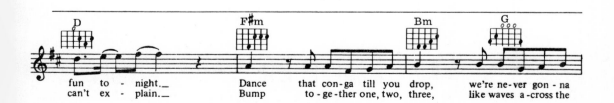

fun to - night.__ Dance that con - ga till you drop, we're ne - ver gon - na
can't ex - plain.__ Bump to - ge-ther one, two, three, like waves a -cross the

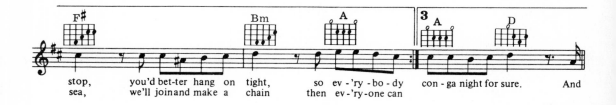

stop, you'd bet-ter hang on tight, so ev-'ry-bo-dy con-ga night for sure. And

sea, we'll join and make a chain then ev-'ry-one can

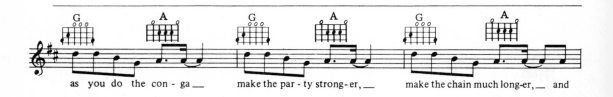

as you do the con-ga __ make the par-ty strong-er, __ make the chain much long-er, __ and

do the, do the, do the, do the con-ga night. Do do __ do, __ come

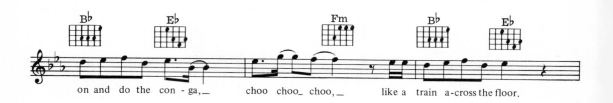

on and do the con-ga, __ choo choo __ choo, __ like a train a-cross the floor.

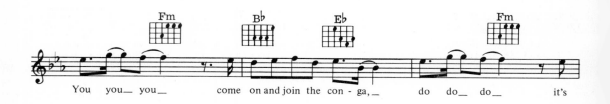

You you __ you __ come on and join the con-ga, __ do do __ do __ it's

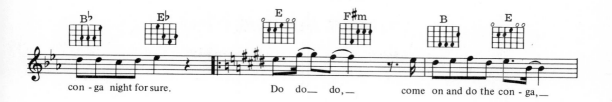

con - ga night for sure.   Do do— do, —   come on and do the con - ga, —

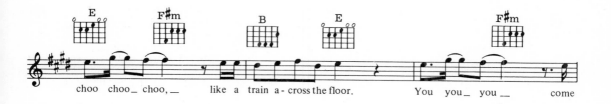

choo choo— choo, —   like a train a - cross the floor.   You you— you —   come

on and join the con - ga, —   do do— do —   it's con - ga night for sure.   And

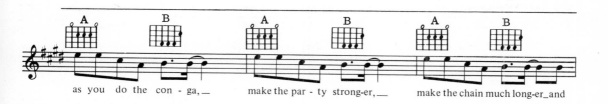

as you do the con - ga, —   make the par - ty strong-er, —   make the chain much long-er— and

do the, do the, do the, do the   con - ga night for sure.

18
Don't You
(Forget About Me)

Words & Music by Keith Forsey & Steve Schiff

19
Drive

Words & Music by Ric Ocasek

20
EastEnders
(Theme from 'EastEnders')

By Leslie Osborne & Simon May

21
Easy Lover

Words by Phil Collins
Music by Phil Collins, Philip Bailey & Nathan East

22
Election Day

Words & Music by Taylor, Rhodes & Le Bon

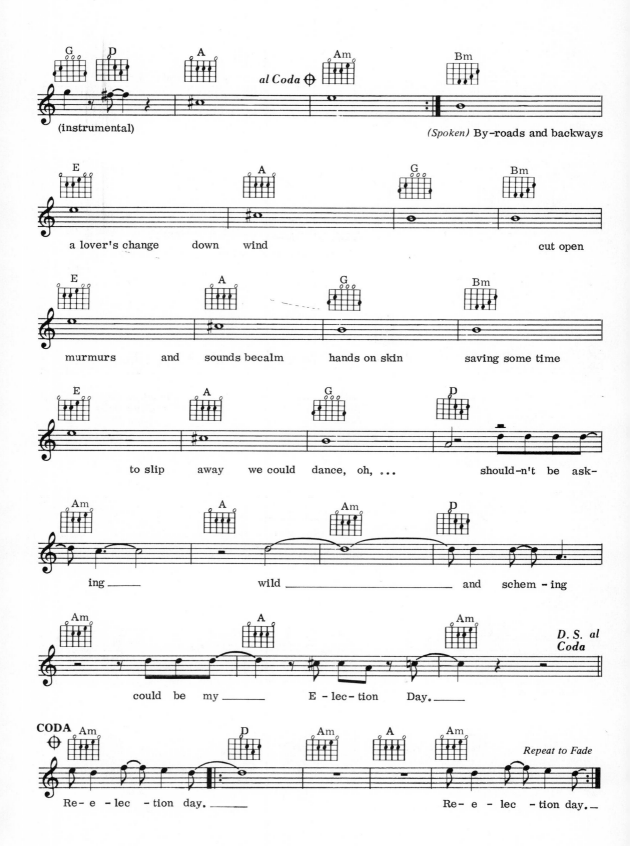

23
Gold

Words & Music by Gary Kemp

Moderato

Thank you for com-ing__ home. I'm
Af-ter the rush has__ gone I

sor-ry that the chairs are all__ worn.__ I left them here I could have sworn.__
hope you find a lit-tle more__ time.__ Re-mem-ber we were part-ners in__ crime.__

These are my sal-ad__ days slow-ly be-ing eat-en a__ way.__
It's on-ly two years a-go the man with the suit and the__ pace__ You

Just an-oth-er play for to-day. Oh but I'm proud of you__ but I'm proud of you.__
knew that he was there on the case. Now he's in love with you__ he's in love with you.__ My

Noth-ing left to make me feel__ small.__ Luck has left me stand-ing so__ tall,__
love is like a high pri-son wall and you could leave me stand-ing so__ tall,__

24
Feel Like Making Love

Words & Music by Eugene McDaniels

Moderato

1. Strol-lin' in ___ the park ___ watch-in' win-ter turn to spring ___
3. In a rest - au - rant ___ hold-in' hands by can - dle - light ___

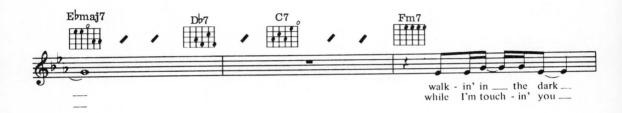

walk - in' in ___ the dark ___
while I'm touch - in' you ___

see - in' lov - ers do their thing ___   ooh ___
want - in' you ___ with all my might ___

___ that's the time ___   I feel like mak - in' love   to you ___

___   That's the time ___   I feel like mak - in'

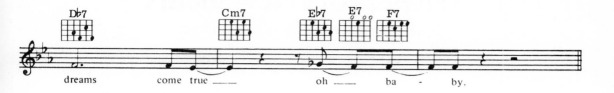

dreams   come true ____   oh ____ ba - by.

2. When you talk __ to me   when you're moan - in' sweet and low ___
4. Strol - lin' in __ the park   watch - in' win - ter turn to spring _

When you're touch-in' me   and my feel - ings start to show
Walk - in' in the dark   see - in' lov - ers do their thing

ooh   that's the time

(Start fade now)

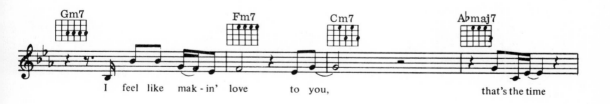

I feel like mak - in' love   to you,   that's the time

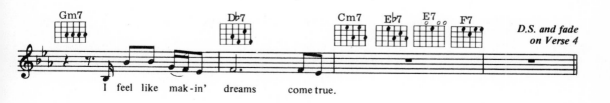

D.S. and fade
on Verse 4

I feel like mak - in' dreams   come true.

25
Friends And Neighbours

Words & Music by Marvin Scott & Malcolm Lockyer

Moderato

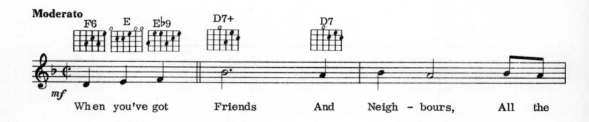

When you've got Friends And Neigh - bours, All the

world is a hap - pi - er place. Friends And Neigh-bours, Put a

smile on the gloom - i - est face. Just take your lit - tle

troub-les and share 'em, With the folks next door, Makes it twice as

eas - y to bear 'em, That's what friends are for 'cos if you've

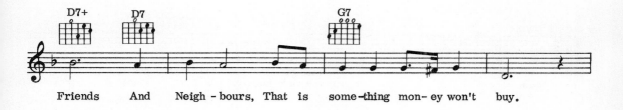

Friends And Neigh-bours, That is some-thing mon-ey won't buy.

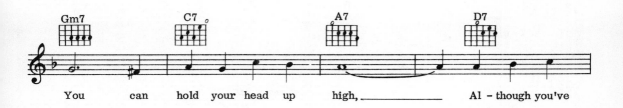

You can hold your head up high, _____ Al - though you've

not a pen - ny, And your house may be tum-ble-ing down, With

Friends And Neigh-bours, You're the rich-est man in town. ____

26
Gloria

Words & Music by Giancarlo Bigazzi & Umberto Tozzi
English Lyrics by Trevor Veitch

27
Goodbye Girl

Words & Music: Peter Cox & Richard Drummie

Moderato

Foot-steps ech-o on fam - il - iar streets,___ cross-ing brid - ges, ne - ver

burned._____ I am tired of play - ing hide and seek___

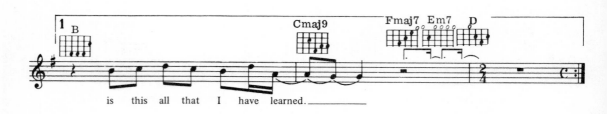

is this all that I have learned._____

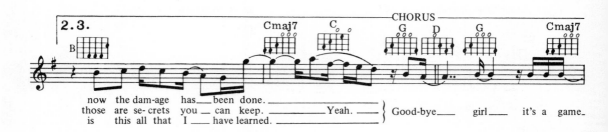

now the dam-age has___ been done._____
those are se - crets you ___ can keep._____ Yeah. ___ } Good-bye___ girl___ it's a game___
is this all that I ___ have learned. _____

_ we play_ ev-'ry-time_we say_good-bye_ girl,_ you hypno-tise,_____ I can't

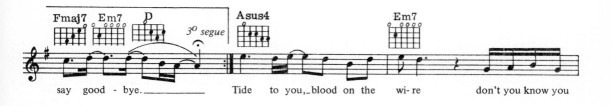

say good-bye._____ Tide to you,_blood on the wi-re don't you know you

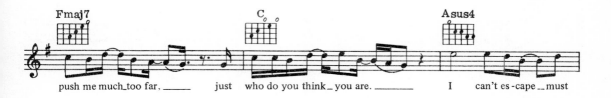

push me much_too far,_____ just who do you think_you are._____ I can't es-cape_must

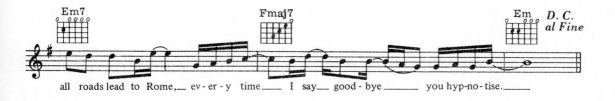

all roads lead to Rome,_ ev-er-y time____ I say_ good-bye_____ you hyp-no-tise._____

VERSE 2:
Looking for a diamond in the dark,
I was sure you were the one.
You held me spell-bound while you made your mark
Those are secrets you can keep, yeah.

VERSE 3:
I'm afraid when I turn out the light
Words you say while you're asleep.
Where you were and what you did last night
Is this all that I have learned?

28
Happy Xmas (War Is Over)

Words & Music by John Lennon & Yoko Ono

29
Hard To Say I'm Sorry

Words & Music by P. Cetera & D. Foster

Moderato

mf Ev-'ry-bo-dy needs a lit-tle time a-way,___ I've heard her say,___
Could-n't stand to be kept a-way,___ Just for the day,___

___ from each oth - er. Ev-en lov-ers need a hol-i-day,
___ from your bo - dy. . Would-n't want to be swept a-way,-

___ Far a-way___ from each oth - er.
___ Far a-way___ from the one that I love.

Hold me now,___ it's hard for me to say I'm sor-ry,
Hold me now,___ it's hard for me to say I'm sor-ry,

I just want you___ to stay.___ | Aft-er all___ that we've been
I just want you___ to know.___ {

through, I will make it up_____ to you, I pro - mise to,

30
Hey, Mr Music Man

English lyrics by Bryan Blackburn
Music by Gunther-Eric Thoner

31
Hi De Hi Holiday Rock
(Theme from 'Hi De Hi')

Words & Music by Jimmy Perry

mf Well if you're feel-ing lone-ly, And get-ting in __ a stew, Just

bend your ear, come ov-er here and man __ here's what you do. If you got the blues,

I got the news, join in the fun in your blue suede shoes, __ Do the

hol-i-day rock, (hol-i-day rock) do the hol-i-day rock, (hol-i-day rock)

Hi-de-hi-de-hi, ho-de-ho-de-ho, go, go, go, do the hol-i-day rock.

Sum-mer time comes, work's such a bore, get on the train with the
Can't get a chick, don't know the trick, we're on the way, you can

32
Hole In My Shoe

Words & Music by Dave Mason

Spoken: Hello shoes, I'm sorry but I'm gonna have to stand on you again. Eugh!
Oh wow! What a horrible dream I just had.
Oh no! What a really heavy bummer.

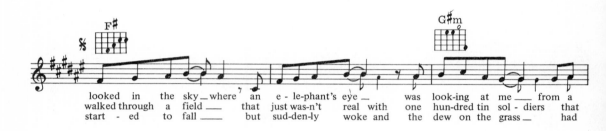

looked in the sky __ where an e - le-phant's eye __ was look-ing at me __ from a
walked through a field __ that just was-n't real with one hun-dred tin sol - diers that
start - ed to fall __ but sud-den-ly woke and the dew on the grass __ had

bub - ble - gum tree __
stood at my shoul-ders } and all that I knew __ was the hole in my shoe __ which was
soaked through my coat __

To Coda

let - ting in wa - ter, let - ting in wa - ter, __ let - ting in wa - ter.

Oh no! What's happening?

(Spoken) I climbed on the back of a giant anchovy and flew off through a gap in the clouds to a land where music

was playing incredibly loudly, and everyone was really happy and having a really good time, except me.

D.S.

CODA

Spoken – to fade

Oh what an amazingly beautiful vibe.
I think I'm gonna get in the bath with my shoes on
'Cause like it won't make any difference right oh wow.
Hey I feel like I'm just floating.
Is anyone lighting a joss stick?
I must be a pretty amazing guy though to have dreamed all this,
Maybe it's because I ate all that cheese I found under the cooker.
Oh no hang on oh I must be back in reality again.
Oh no look at all that washing up. Heavy.

33
I Feel For You

Words & Music by Prince

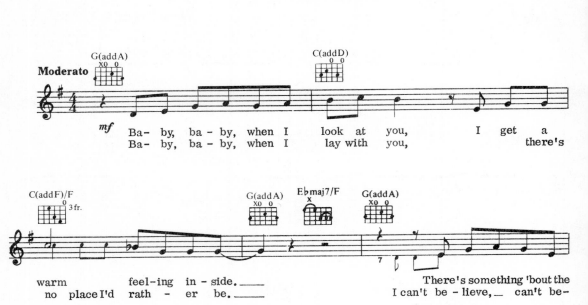

Ba - by, ba - by, when I look at you, I get a
Ba - by, ba - by, when I lay with you, there's

warm feel-ing in - side. ___ There's something 'bout the
no place I'd rath - er be. ___ I can't be - lieve, ___ can't be-

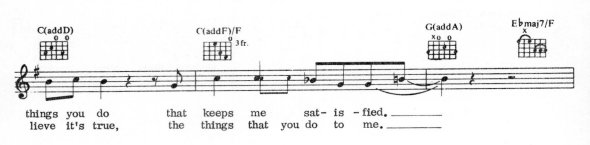

things you do that keeps me sat - is - fied. ___
lieve it's true, the things that you do to me. ___

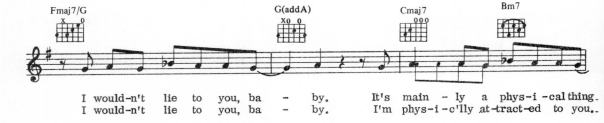

I would-n't lie to you, ba - by. It's main - ly a phys-i-cal thing.
I would-n't lie to you, ba - by. I'm phys-i-c'lly at-tract-ed to you. ___

___ This feel-ing that I got for you, ba - by, it
___ This feel-ing that I got for you, ba - by, there's

34
If Leaving Me Is Easy

Words & Music by Phil Collins

I read all the let - ters,__ I read each word__ that you've sent

__ to me; And though it's past now,__ And your words start to

fade __ All the mem'ries_I've had__ still re - main.__

I've kept all the pic - tures __ But I hide my feel - ings__ so
You see I'd heard the ru - mours__ I knew be - fore_____ you

no one knows.___ Oh sure my friends all ___ come
let me know.___ But I did-n't be-lieve it, ___ not

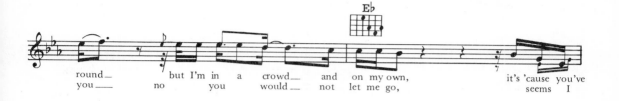

round ___ but I'm in a crowd ___ and on my own, it's 'cause you've
you ___ no you would ___ not let me go, seems I

gone now, ___ But your heart, heart still re-mains ___ And it-'ll
was wrong, ___ But I love, love you the same ___ And that's the

be here if ___ you ___ come a-gain. ___
one thing that you ___ can't take a - -way, ___ But just re-

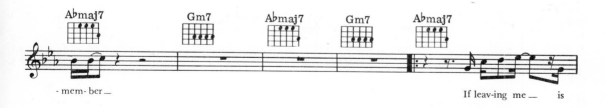

- mem-ber ___ If leav-ing me ___ is

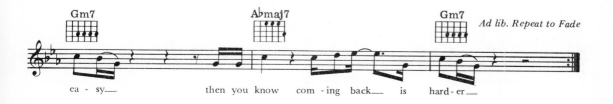

Ad lib. Repeat to Fade

ea-sy ___ then you know com-ing back ___ is hard-er ___

35
If You Love Somebody Set Them Free

Words & Music by Sting

If it's a mirror you want, just look into my eyes,
Or a whipping boy, someone to despise,
Or a prisoner in the dark,
Tied up in chains you just can't see,
Or a beast in a guilded cage,
That's all some people ever want to be.

36
I Got You Babe

Words & Music by Sonny Bono

37
I Know Him So Well

Words & Music by
Benny Andersson, Tim Rice & Bjorn Ulvaeus

38
In The Air Tonight

Words & Music by Phil Collins

you told me— you were drown-ing,   I would not lend— a hand.
mem-ber,   I re - mem-ber, don't— wor - ry,   How could I

I've seen your face— be-fore, my— friend, But I don't
ev - er for - get it's the first— time—   the last time— we

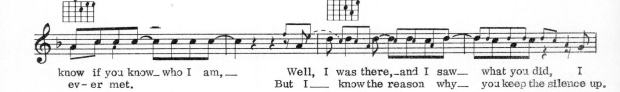

know if you know— who I am, —   Well, I was there, —and I saw— what you did, I
ev - er met.   But I— know the reason why— you keep the silence up.

saw it with my own two eyes.—   So you can wipe of that grin,   I
     No you don't fool me.   The hurt doesn't show,   but the

know where you've been, —   It's all been a pack of lies.
pain — still grows, — it's no stran-ger to you— or me.

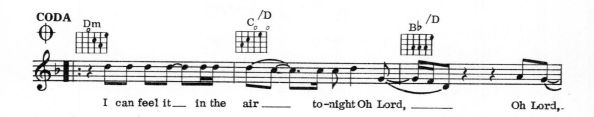

CODA

I can feel it___ in the air___ to-night Oh Lord, ___ Oh Lord,-

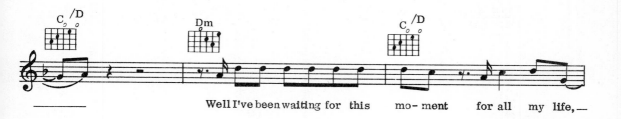

___ Well I've been waiting for this mo-ment for all my life, ___

Oh Lord, ___ And I can feel it com-

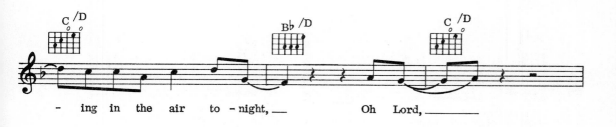

- ing in the air to-night, ___ Oh Lord, ___

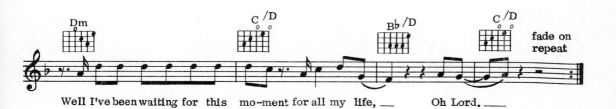

Well I've been waiting for this mo-ment for all my life, ___ Oh Lord. ___

39
In Your Eyes

Words & Music by Dan Hill & Michael Masser

think I final - ly know__ you,   I can see be - yond__ your smile,   I
warned me that life chang - es,   that no one real - ly knows   whe-ther

think that I__ can show__ you   that what we have is still__ worth-while. Don't you know that
time would make__ us stran - gers   or whe-ther time would make__ us grow. Ev - en though the

love's just like the thread__   that keeps un - rav - el - ing,__ but then__   it
winds of time will change__ in a world where no - thing stays__ the same.__

ties us back__ to - geth - er in the end.   In your__
Through it all__ our love will still re - main.

40
I Should Have Known Better

Words & Music by Jim Diamond & Graham Lyle

fooled a-round___ but tell me now___ just who is hurt-ing who?___
now there is ___ no chance you'll come_ back home, got too much pride.___

D. S. al
Coda

CODA

And I should have known

Can you for - give me?

I_ I I I I_ I I   I I I_ should have known better_ I_ I I I I_ I I

I I I_ should have known_ bet-ter.___

1. It's
2.

La la la   la la la la la   la____ I love   you.__   La la la la la

la,____ yeah,___   And I should have known bet-ter   to

lie with one as beaut - i -ful as   you.___

41
Into The Groove

Words & Music by Madonna Ciccone & Steve Bray

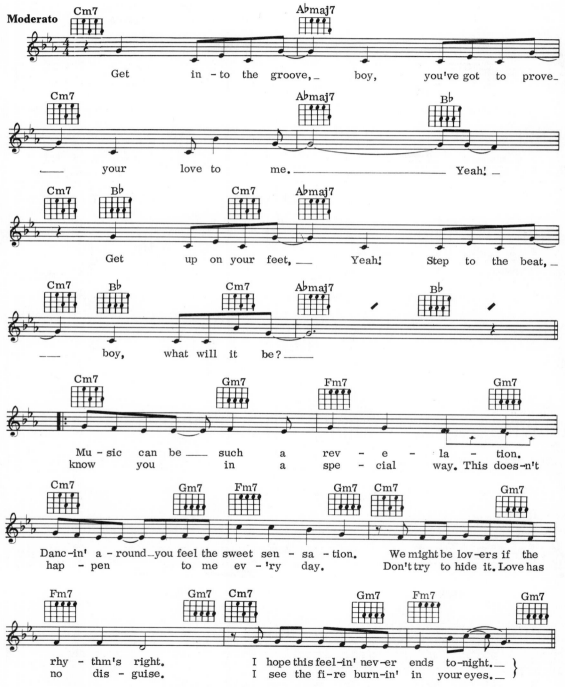

42
Is There Something I Should Know?

Words & Music by Duran Duran

43
I Won't Let The Sun Go Down On Me

Words & Music by Nik Kershaw

For - ty winks in the lob - by, make mine a G. and T.
Moth-er na - ture is-n't in it, three hun - dred mil - lion years.

Then to our fav - 'rite hob - by search - ing for an en - e - my.
Good - bye in just a min - ute, gone for ev - er, no more tears.

Here in our pa - per hou - ses, stretch - ing for miles and miles.
Pin - ball man, pow - er glut - ton, vac - uum in - side his head.

Old men in strip-ey trou - sers rule the world with plas-tic smiles.
Fore-fin - ger on the but - ton, Is he blue or is he red.

Good or __ bad, like it or __ not,
Break your __ si - lence if you __ would be-

44
January, February

Words & Music by Alan Tarney

road___ to one more _ brok - en heart.___

CHORUS

___ Jan - u - ar - y, Feb - ru - a - ry, I don't un - der -

- stand why it is you say you're leav - ing, then you turn a - round, you

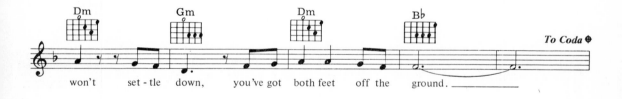

To Coda ⊕

won't set - tle down, you've got both feet off the ground. _____

Jan - u - ar - y, Feb - ru - ar - y don't you come a - round.

D.%. al Coda

It

⊕ CODA

(Repeat to Fade)

Jan - u - ar - y, Feb - ru - ar - y don't you come a - round.

45
Karma Chameleon

Words & Music by O'Dowd, Moss, Hay, Craig & Pickett

Desert lov-ing in your eyes___ all___ the way.___
2. Hear your wick-ed words___ ev-'ry day.___

If___ I___ lis-ten to___ your lies___ would___ you___ say.
And___ you___ used to be so sweet___ I heard you___ say.

I'm___ a man___ with-out___ con-vic-tion,___
That___ my love___ was an___ a-ddic-tion,___

I'm___ a man___ who does-n't know,
When___ we cling___ our love___ is strong,

How___ to sell___ a con-tra-dic-tion,___
When___ you go___ you're gone for-ev-er,___

You come___ and go, You come___ and go.___
You string___ a-long, You string___ a-long.___

46
Ladies Night

Words & Music by George Brown & Kool & The Gang

Gon-na step out, Lad-ies Night,— Steppin' out, Lad-ies Night. Oh yes, it's

D. S. al Coda

CODA

Oh dis-co lights your name will be seen.__

You can ful-fill all_____ your dreams.__ Par-ty here,— par-ty there,—

ev-'ry-where, ___ this is your night_ ba-by,— you've got to be there. __

This is your night to - night; Ev-'ry-thing's gon-na be al - right.

Repeat and fade

This is your night to - night; Ev-'ry-thing's gon-na be al - right.

Verse 2:

Romantic lady, single baby, mm,
Sophisticated mama.
Come on, you disco lady, yeah,
Stay with me tonight, mama.

(To Bridge:)

47
Lady Love Me (One More Time)

Words & Music by James Newton Howard & David Paich

48
Let The Music Play

Words & Music by Ed Chisolm & Chris Barbosa

Moderate funk

1. We start-ed danc-ing and love put us in-to a groove, as
2. The mu-sic played while our bod-ies dis-played through the dance that
3.(See additional lyrics)

1. soon as we start-ed to move.

2.3. love picked us out for ro-mance.

I thought it was clear the plan_____ was we would share this feel-ing just be-tween our-selves._____ But when the mu-sic changed, the plan__ was re-ar-ranged; he went to dance with some-one____ else.____

We start-ed danc-ing, and love put us in-to a groove. But

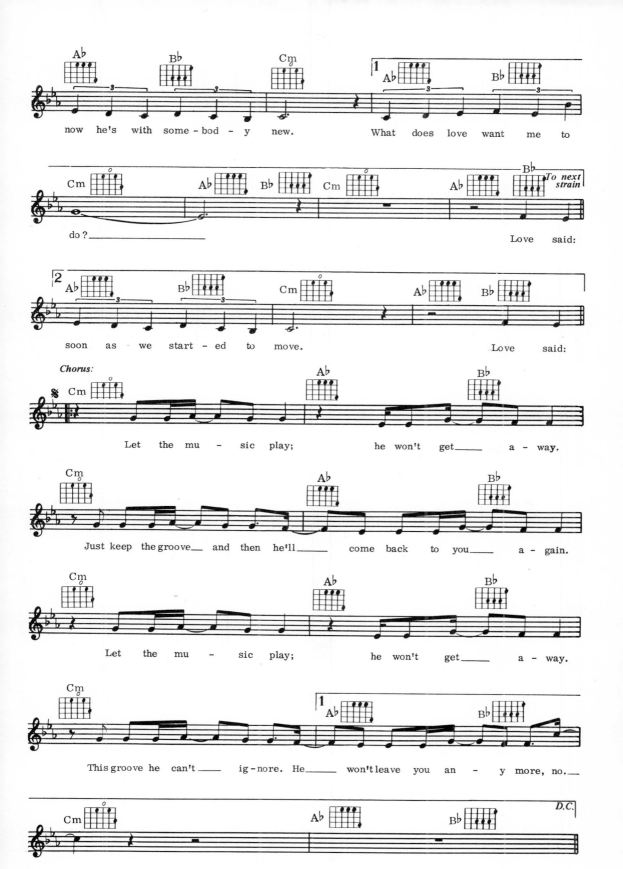

won't leave you an - y more, no.

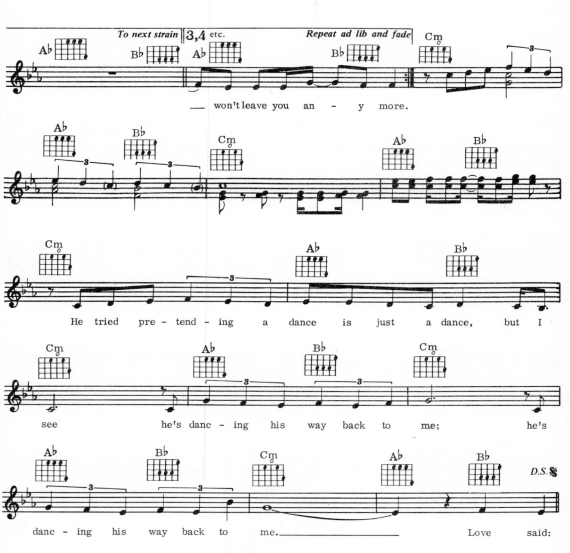

To next strain ‖3,4 etc.   **Repeat ad lib and fade**

won't leave you an - y more.

He tried pre - tend - ing a dance is just a dance, but I

see he's danc - ing his way back to me; he's

danc - ing his way back to me._____ Love said:

Verse 3:
He tried pretending a dance is just a dance, but I see
He's dancing his way back to me.
Guess he's discovered
We are truly lovers;
Magic from the very start. 'Cause
Love just kept me groovin', and
He felt me movin'
Even though we danced apart.
So we started dancing and love put us back in the groove
As soon as we started to move,
As soon as we started to move. _(To Chorus:)_

49
Little April Shower

Words by Larry Morey
Music by Frank Churchill

Drip drip drop, Lit-tle A-pril Show-er, beat-ing a tune as you fall all a-round.
Drip drip drop, Lit-tle A-pril Show-er, beat-ing a tune ev-'ry-where that you fall.

Drip drip drop, Lit-tle A-pril Show-er, what can compare with your beau-ti-ful sound.
Drip drip drop, Lit-tle A-pril Show-er, I'm get-ting wet and I don't care at all.

Drip drip drop, when the sky is cloud-y, your pret-ty mu-sic can bright-en the day.

Drip drip drop, when the sun says "How-dy", you say "Good-bye" right a-way. ___

CODA

Drip! Drop! Drip! Drop! I'll nev-er be a-

fraid of a good lit-tle gay lit-tle A-pril ser-e-nade.

50
Love And Pride

Words & Music by P. King & M. Roberts

Moderato

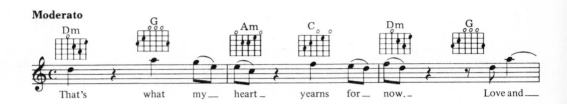

That's what my heart yearns for now. Love and

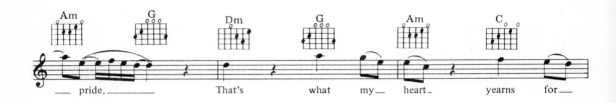

pride. That's what my heart yearns for

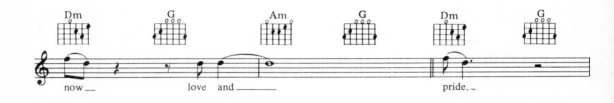

now love and pride.

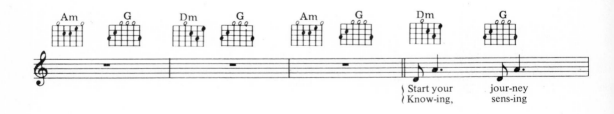

Start your journey
Know-ing, sens-ing

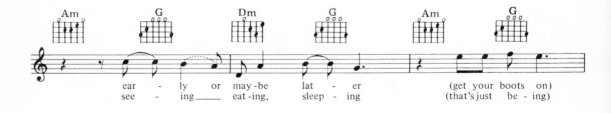

ear-ly or may-be lat-er (get your boots on)
see-ing eat-ing, sleep-ing (that's just be-ing)

51
More Than I Can Say

Words & Music by Sonny Curtis & Jerry Allison

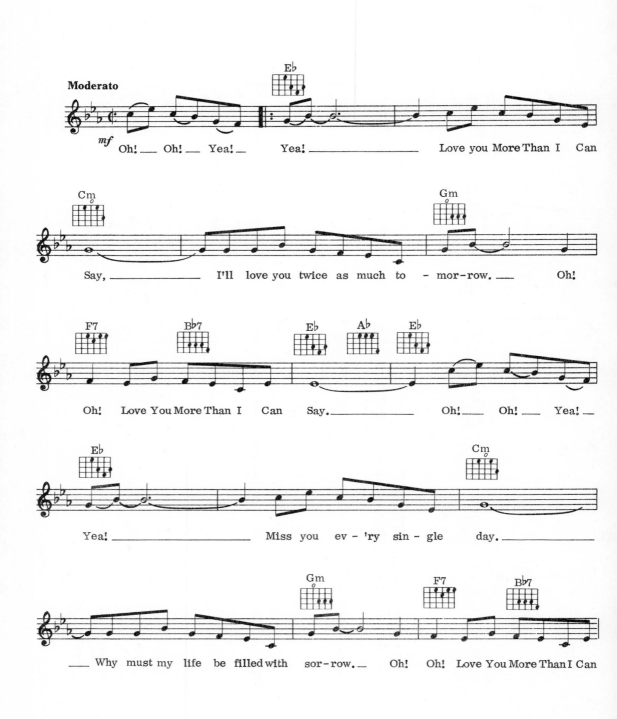

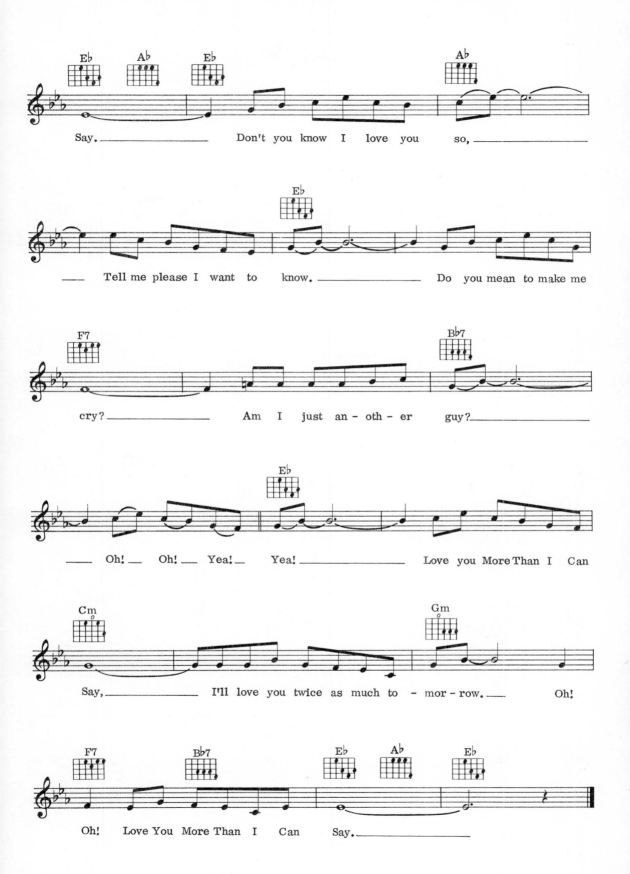

52
Lucille

Words & Music by Albert Collins and Richard Penniman

Lu - cille,
cille,
cille,

Won't you do your sis - ter's
Please come back where you be -
Ba - by sat - is - fy my

will?
long.
heart.

Oh, Lu - cille,
Oh, Lu - cille,
Oh, Lu - cille,

Won't you do your sis - ter's will?
Please come back where you be - long.
Ba - by, sat - is - fy my heart.

Well, you
I been
I

ran a - way and left,
good to you ba - by,
slaved for you, ba - by,

I love you still
Please don't leave me a - lone.
And gave you such a won - der - ful start.

Lu-
Lu-

Spoken

I

woke up this morn — ing, Lu — cille was not in sight. I

asked her friends a - bout her, But all their lips were tight. Lu-

cille,_____ Please come back where you be - long,_____

I been good to you ba - by, Please don't leave me a - lone-

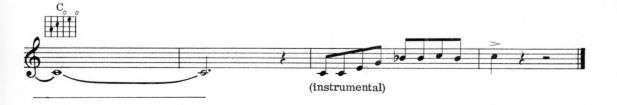

(instrumental)

53
Merry Christmas Everybody

Words & Music by Neville Holder & James Lea

54
Miami Vice
(Theme from 'Miami Vice')

By Jan Hammer

55
Money For Nothing

Words & Music by Mark Knopfler & Sting

1. Look at them yo-yo's that's — the way to do it —
5.(%) I shoulda — learned to — play the gui-tar —
7.(%%) Look at them yo-yo's that's — the way to do it —

play the gui-tar on the M. T. V. that ain't — work-in' that's
I shoulda learned to play them drums look at that she got it
play the gui-tar on the M.. T. V. that ain't — work-in' that's

— the way to do it mon-ey for noth-in' and chicks for free.—
stickin' in the camera man we could have some fun.—
— the way you do it money for noth-in' and chicks for free.—

2. That ain't work-in' that's — the way you do it lem-me tell ya them —
3. See that little faggot with the ear-ring and the make up yeah buddy that's
4. INSTR. to Chorus _____
6.(%) And he's up there he's making Hawaiian noises bangin' on the bongos like a

56
Never Gonna Let You Go

Words by Cynthia Weil
Music by Barry Mann

Moderato

I was as wrong____ as I____ could____ be____ to let you get____
Look-ing back now,____ it seems____ so____ clear,____ I had it all____

____ a - way____ from me;____ I'll re - gret that____ move____ for as
____ when you____ were____ here;____ Oh you gave it____ all____ and I

long as I'm liv - ing.____ But now that I've come____
took it for grant - ed.____ But if there's some feel -

____ to see____ the light,____ all I wan-na do____ is make____ things____
ing left____ in you,____ some flick-er of love____ that still____ shines

right, so just say the word____ and tell me that I'm____ for - giv -
through, let's talk it out,____ let's talk a - bout sec - ond chanc -

en. You and me,____ we're gon - na be bet - ter
es. Wait and see,____ it's gon - na be sweet - er

57
Nightshift

Words & Music by
Dennis Lambert, Franne Golde & Walter Orange

58
One More Night

Words & Music by Phil Collins

59
Only You

Words & Music by Vincent Clarke

Moderato

1. Look-ing from a win-dow a-bove is like a sto-ry of love,___
2. Some-times when I think of her name, when it's on-ly a game,___
3. This is gon-na take a long time and I won-der what's mine___

___ can you hear___ me? Came back on-ly yes-ter- day,___
___ and I need___ you. Lis-ten to the words that you say,___
___ can't take___ no more. Won-der if you'll un-der - stand,

___ we're mov-ing fath-er a - way, ___ want you near___ me.
___ it's get-ting hard-er to stay ___ when I see ___ you.
___ it's just the touch of your hand___ be-hind closed ___ door.

All I need-ed was the love you gave,___ all I need-ed for an -

oth - er day, ___ and all I ev - er knew___ on-ly you.

1-2 A

3 A

60
Physical

Words & Music by Steve Kipner & Terry Shaddick

61
Please Don't Fall In Love

Words & Music by Mike Batt

love.

I'm us - ual - ly strong __ but I'm
We kissed at the air - port, we

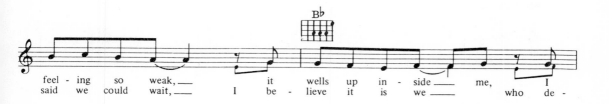

feel - ing so weak, ___ it wells up in - side __ me, I
said we could wait, ___ I be - lieve it is we __ who de -

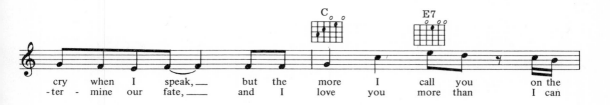

cry when I speak, ___ but the more I call you on the
-ter - mine our fate, ___ and I love you more than I can

phone the more I feel a - lone and the less we have to
say, don't throw it all a - way, don't let it go by. ___

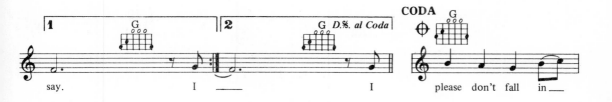

say. I ___ I please don't fall in __

love.

62
The Power Of Love

Words & Music by
C. de Rouge, G. Mende, J. Rush & S. Applegate

Moderato

The whis-pers in the morn-ing ___ of lo - vers sleep-ing tight, are roll-ing by like

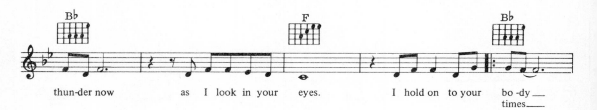

thun-der now as I look in your eyes. I hold on to your bo -dy ___
times ___

and feel each move you make; Your voice is warm and ten-der, A love that I could not for -
it seems I'm far a - way; But ne- ver won-der where I am 'cause I am al -ways by your

sake.⎱
side.⎰ 'Cause I am your lad - y ___ and you are my man, ___

When ev-er you reach for me ⎰ I'll do all that I can. ___ Ev-en though there may be
         ⎱ (I'm gon-na do)

We're head-ing for some-thing, some-where I've ne-ver been, ___ Some-times I am fright-

- ened but I'm read-y to learn __ 'bout the po-wer of love. __

The sound of your heart beat-ing ___ made it clear sud-den-ly. The feel-ing that I

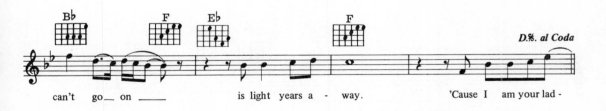

can't go _ on ___ is light years a - way. 'Cause I am your lad -

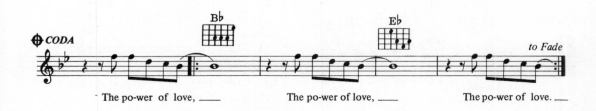

The po-wer of love, ___ The po-wer of love, ___ The po-wer of love. __

63
Private Dancer

Words & Music by Mark Knopfler

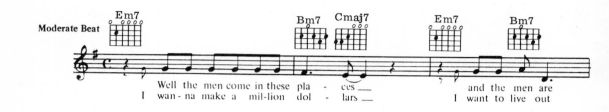

Well the men come in these pla - ces ___ and the men are
I wan - na make a mil - lion dol - lars ___ I want to live out

all the same. ___ You don't look at their fac - es ___ and you don't
by the sea. ___ Have a hus-band and some chil - dren ___ yeah I guess I want a

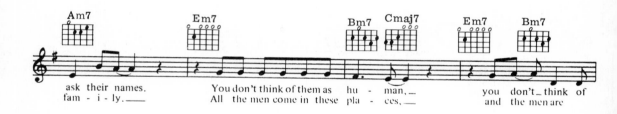

ask their names. You don't think of them as hu - man, ___ you don't_ think of
fam - i - ly. ___ All the men come in these pla - ces, ___ and the men are

them at all, you keep your mind on the mon - ey, ___ keep-ing your eyes
all the same, you don't look at their fac - es, ___ and you don't

on the wall. ___ { I'm your pri - vate dan - cer, a dan-cer for mo-ney, I'll do what you want me to
ask their names. ___ {

64
The Reflex

Words & Music by Duran Duran

(To FADE on Chorus)

65
Reilly
(Theme from 'Reilly')

Based on 'Romance' by Shostakovich
Arranged by Harry Rabinowitz

66
Rhythm Of The Night

Words & Music by Dianne Warren

67
Riders On The Storm

Words & Music by Jim Morrison & The Doors

give this man a ride, sweet fam-i-ly will die. Kill-er on the road.
world on you de-pends, our life will nev-er end. Got-ta love your man.

Ri - ders On The Storm,

Ri - ders On The Storm,

Ri - ders On The Storm,

Ri - ders On The Storm

(instrumental)

68
Running With The Night

Words & Music by C. Weil & L. Richie

69
Run To You

Words & Music by Adams/Vallance

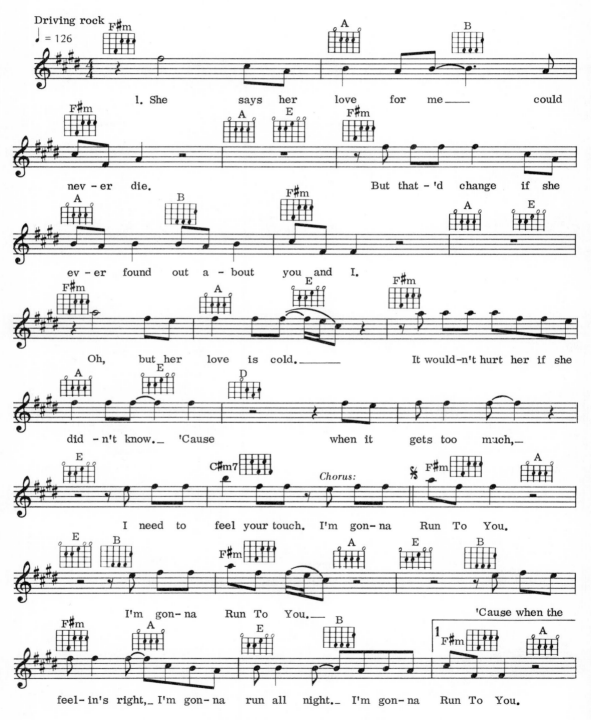

Run To You. Yeah, __ gon-na

Run To You. _____ Oh, __ when the

feel-in's right, __ I'm gon-na run all night, __ I'm gon-na Run To You. __

Run To You. Yeah, __ gon-na

(instrumental)

Oh, gon-na

Verse 2:
She's got a heart of gold,
She'd never let me down.
But you're the one that always turns me on
And keep me comin' 'round.
I know her love is true,
But it's so damn easy makin' love to you.
I got my mind made up,
I need to feel your touch.

(To Chorus:)

70
Sam

Words & Music by
John Farrar, Hank Marvin & Don Black

71
Shout

Words & Music by Roland Orzabal & Ian Stanley

Moderately slow.
(Double time feel)

Shout, Shout, Let it all out.___ These are the things I can

do with - out.___ Come on, ___ I'm talk - ing to you, ___ Come on. ___

VERSE

1. In vio - lent times, ___

You shouldn't have to sell your soul ___ in black ___

___ and white, ___ They real - ly real - ly ought to know. ___

© Copyright 1985 Virgin Music (Publishers) Limited and 10 Music Limited, London W11.
All Rights Reserved. International Copyright Secured.

72
The Show
(Theme from 'Connie')

Words by Willy Russell & Ron Hutchinson
Music by Willy Russell

Verse 2:

I never read books,
They're just Latin and Greek,
I'm more into looks,
Silk, satin and the chic I know,
I'm putting on The Show.

73
Slave To Love

Words & Music by Bryan Ferry

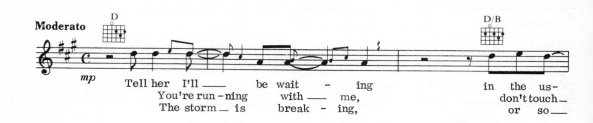

Moderato

Tell her I'll ___ be wait - ing   in the us-don't touch___
You're run - ning   with ___ me,
The storm ___ is   break - ing,   or so

___ ual   place,   With the tired ___   and wea - ry,
___ the   ground,   We're the rest - less heart - ed,
___ it   seems,   We're too young ___   to rea - son,

And there's   no es - cape. ___   To need ___
Not the   chained and bound. ___   The
Too grown   up to dream. ___   Now

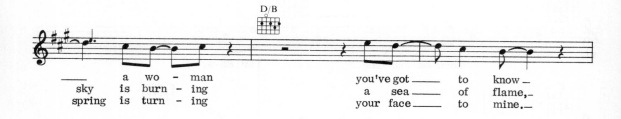

___ a wo - man   you've got ___   to know ___
sky   is burn - ing   a   sea ___   of   flame, ___
spring is turn - ing   your face ___   to   mine. ___

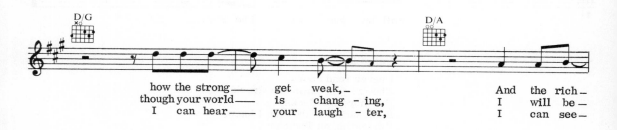

how the strong ___   get   weak, ___   And the rich ___
though your world ___   is   chang - ing,   I   will   be ___
I   can hear ___   your   laugh - ter,   I   can   see ___

© Copyright 1985 EG Music Limited, 63a Kings Road, London SW3.
All Rights Reserved. International Copyright Secured.

74
So Far Away

Words & Music by Mark Knopfler

Moderato

mf

I'm
And I

Here I am a - gain in this mean old town, ___
tired of being in love and be - ing all a - lone, ___
get so tired when I have to ex - plain,

and you're So Far A - way ___ from me. Now
when you're So Far A - way ___ from me. I'm
when you're So Far A - way ___ from me. See

where are you when the sun goes down, ___
tired of ma - king out on the tel - e - phone, ___
you've been in the sun and I've been in the rain,

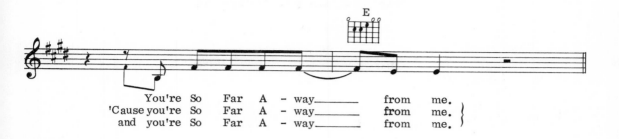

You're So Far A - way_____ from me.
'Cause you're So Far A - way_____ from me.
and you're So Far A - way_____ from me.

You're So Far A - way from me.__ You're so far I

just can't see. You're So Far A - way from me.__

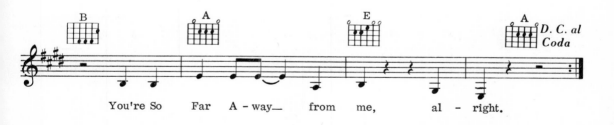

D. C. al Coda

You're So Far A - way__ from me, al - right.

CODA

Repeat ad lib. to fade

You're So Far A - way__ from me.

75
Some Like It Hot

Words & Music by R. Palmer, A. Taylor & J. Taylor

76
Sometimes

Words by Norman Newell
Music by Carl Davis

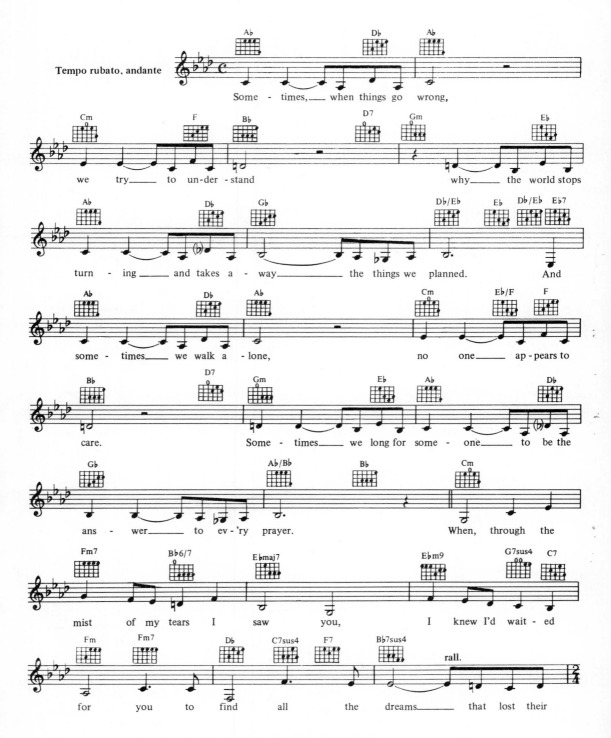

77
On The Wings Of Love

Words by Jeffrey Osborne
Music by Peter Schless

Verse 2:
You look at me and I begin to melt
Just like the snow, when a ray of sun is felt.
And I'm crazy 'bout you, baby, can't you see?
I'd be so delighted if you would come with me.
(To Chorus:)

78
Spice Of Life

Words & Music by Rod Temperton & Derek Bramble

79
Street Life

Words by Will Jennings
Music by Joe Sample

80
Suddenly

Words & Music by Keith Diamond & Billy Ocean

I used to think that love _ was just _ a fai-ry tale un-til that first hel-lo, _

un-til that first _ smile. But if I had to do it all a-gain, _

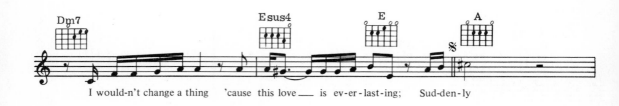

I would-n't change a thing 'cause this love _ is ev-er-last-ing; Sud-den-ly

life has new mean-ing _ to me, there's beau-ty up _ a-bove _ and things we

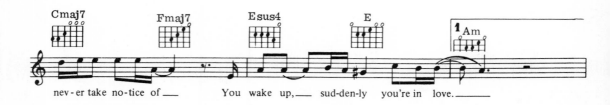

nev-er take no-tice of _ You wake up, _ sud-den-ly you're in love.

Girl you're everything a man could want and more
One thousand words are not enough to say what I feel inside
Holding hands as we walk along the shore
Never felt like this before, now you're all I'm living for

81
Sultans Of Swing

Words & Music by Mark Knopfler

1. You get a shiv-er in the dark, it's__ rain-ing in the park, but mean-
2. step in-side__ but you don't see too man-y fa-

time,
ces

south of the riv-er you stop
com-in' in out of the rain__

and you hold ev-'ry-thing._____
__ to hear the jazz go down.__

A band is blow-in' Dix-ie dou-ble four____ time.
Com-pe-ti-tion in oth-er plac-es,

You feel all right when you hear the mu-sic ring.__
but the horns, they're blow-in' that

1.3.

sound.

2. Well now, you

Way on down___ south,   way on   down   south

Lon-don Town.___

To Coda

D.S. ℅ for additional Verses
(After last verse, To Coda ⊕)

3. You check out

⊕ *Coda*

Guitar ad lib.

Repeat and fade

3. You check out Guitar George, he knows all the chords.
   Mind he's strictly rhythm, he doesn't want to make it cry or sing.
   This and an old guitar is all he can afford,
     when he gets up under the lights to play his thing.

4. And Harry doesn't mind if he doesn't make the scene.
   He's got a daytime job, he's doin' all right.
   He can play the honky-tonk like anything,
     savin' it up for Friday night
     with the Sultans, with the Sultans of Swing.

5. And a crowd of young boys, they're foolin' around in the corner,
     drunk and dressed in their best brown baggies and their platform soles.
   They don't give a damn about any trumpet playin' band;
     it ain't what they call rock and roll.
   And the Sultans, yeah the Sultans, they played Creole.

6. *Instrumental*

7. And then The Man, he steps right up to the microphone
     and says, at last, just as the time-bell rings:
   "Good night, now it's time to go home."
   And he makes it fast with one more thing:
   "We are the Sultans, we are the Sultans of Swing."
   (To Coda)

82
Sweet Dreams
(Are Made Of This)

Words & Music by A. Lennox & D. A. Stewart

Sweet Dreams are made of this, Who am I to dis-a-gree? I tra-vel the world and the sev-en seas, Ev-'ry-bo-dy's look-ing for some-thing. Some of them want to use you. Some of them want to get used by you. Some of them want to a-buse you. Some of them want to be ab-used.

(instrumental)

hold your head up. Keep your head up, mov-in' on. —

Hold your head up, mov-in' on — Keep your head up, mov-in' on. —

Hold your head up, mov -in' on. — Keep your head up, mov-in' on. —

Hold your head up, mov -in' on, — Keep your head up.

83
That Ole Devil Called Love

Words & Music by Doris Fisher & Allan Roberts

84
That's Livin' Alright
(Theme from 'Auf Wiedersehen Pet')

Words & Music by David Mackay and Ken Ashby

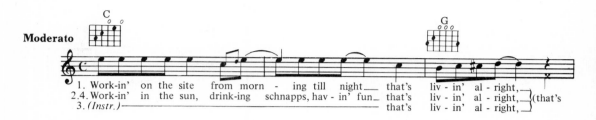

Moderato

1. Work-in' on the site from morn - ing till night___ that's liv-in' al - right,
2.4. Work-in' in the sun, drink-ing schnapps, hav-in' fun___ that's liv-in' al - right,___ (that's
3. (Instr.)————————————————————— that's liv-in' al - right,___

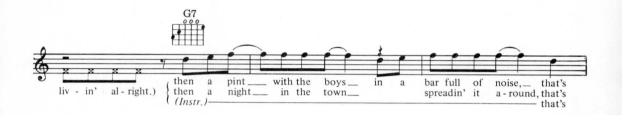

liv-in' al-right.) { then a pint___ with the boys___ in a bar full of noise,___ that's
then a night___ in the town___ spreadin' it a-round, that's
(Instr.)————————————————————————————— that's

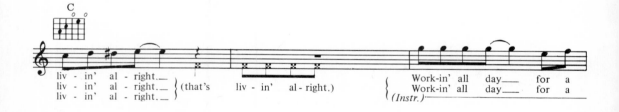

liv-in' al - right.___
liv-in' al - right.___ } (that's liv - in' al - right.)
liv-in' al - right.___

Work-in' all day___ for a
Work-in' all day___ for a
(Instr.)—————————————

pit-tance of pay___ then blow it all on Sat-ur-day night.___ (1.3.) And you
pack-et of pay___ and send a lit-tle back to the wife.___ (2.4.) Still you

kiss the dames___ but you don't ask their names,___ that's liv-in' al - right.___
keep a lit-tle here just to keep you in beer,___ that's liv-in' al - right.

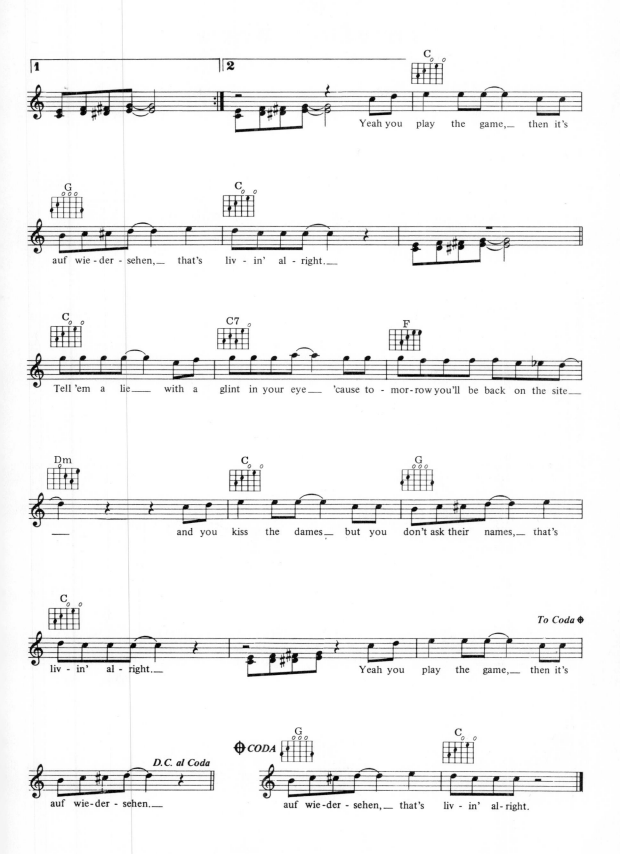

85
They Don't Know

Words & Music by Kirsty McColl

Moderato

mf You've been a - round for such a long time now, __ oh may - be
I get a feel - ing when I look at you __ wher - ev - er
There's no need __ for liv - ing in the past __ and now I've

I could leave __ you but I don't know how. __ And why should I be lone - ly
you go now __ I wan - na be there too. __ They say we're cra - zy but I
found good lov - ing gon - na make it last. __ I tell the oth - ers don't __

ev - 'ry night __ when I can be with you, __ oh yes you make it right, __ and I don't
just don't care and if they keep on talk - ing, still they get no - where, __ so I don't
both - er me 'cause when they look at you, they don't see what I see, __ no I don't

list - en to the guys who say that you're bad for me and I should
mind if they don't un - der - stand when I look at you and you hold __
list - en to their was - ted lines, got my eyes wide o - pen and I __

turn you a - way. __ } 'Cause They Don't Know a - bout us, and
__ my __ hand. __ }
__ see the signs. __

al Coda **1** they've nev - er heard of __ love.

2 love.

© Copyright 1979 Chrysalis Music Limited,
12 Stratford Place, London W1 for the World (excluding USA & Canada).
All Rights Reserved. International Copyright Secured.

86
To All The Girls I've Loved Before

Words & Music by Hal David & Albert Hammond

87
Tonight I Celebrate My Love

Words & Music by Michael Masser & Gerry Goffin

Verse 3:
Tonight I celebrate my love for you,
And soon this old world will seem brand new.
Tonight we will both discover
How friends turn into lovers,
When I make love to you.
(To Chorus:)

88
Take Me Home

Words & Music by Phil Collins

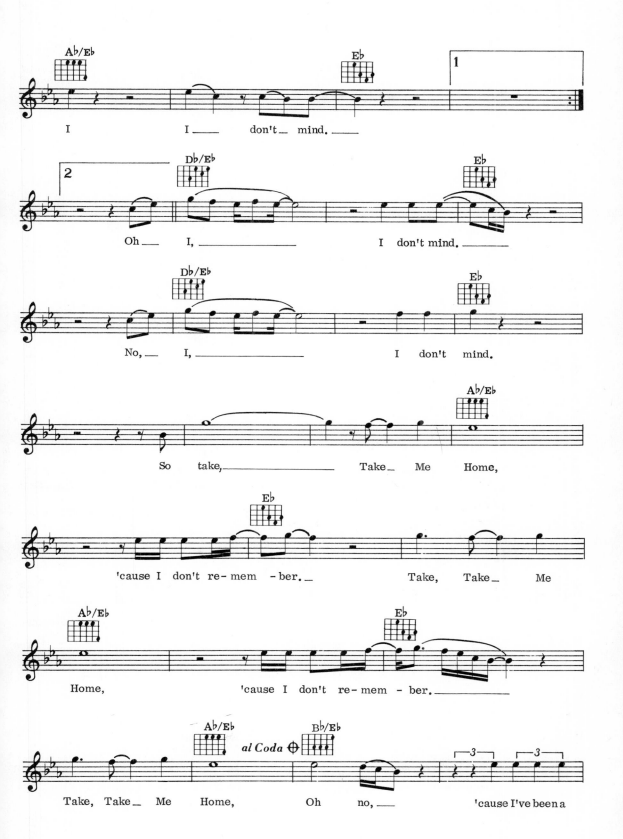

pris-'ner all __ my life. __ And I can say to you, __

CODA

'cause I don't re-mem - ber, __ Take, Take __ Me

Home, Oh no, __ 'cause I've been a

pris'ner all __ my life, __ And I can say to you, __ but I don't re-mem-

ber. __ Take, Take __ Me Home. 'cause I don't re-mem-

VERSE 2

Seems so long I've been waiting
Still don't know what for
There's no point escaping
I don't worry anymore.
I can't come out to find you
I don't like to go outside
They can turn off my feelings
Like they're turning off the light.

But I, *(to Chorus)*

VERSE 3

Take that look of worry
Mine's an ordinary life
Working when it's daylight
And sleeping when it's night.
I've got no far horizons
I don't wish upon a star.
They don't think that I listen
Oh but I know who they are.

And I, *(to Chorus)*

89
True

Words & Music by Gary Kemp

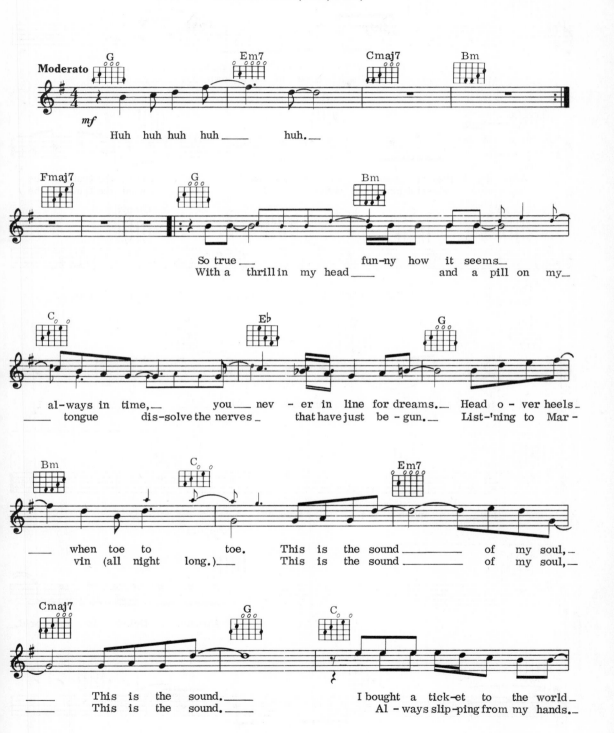

But now I've come back a - gain._____
sand's a time of it's own._____

Why do I find it hard to write the next line?__ Oh I want the truth to be
Take your sea-side arms and write the next line.__ Oh I want the truth to be

said. }
known. } Huh huh huh huh____ huh)__ I know this__

much is__ true._____ Huh huh huh huh_____ huh)____ I

know this__ much is__ true.

I bought a tick-et to the world.__

But now I've come back a-gain._____

90
Take On Me

Words by Morten Harket, Pal Waaktarr & Mags
Music by Pal Waaktarr & Mags

VERSE 2:
So, needless to say at odds and ends
But I'll be stumbling away
Slowly learning that life is O.K.
Say after me
It's much better to be safe than sorry.

VERSE 3:
O, things that you say
Yeah is it life or just a play
My worries away
You're all the things I've got to remember
You shine away
I'll be coming for you anyway.

91
Theme From 'Travelling Man'

By Duncan Browne & Sebastian Graham-Jones

92
20/20

Words & Music by Randy Goodrum & Steve Kipner

When I think of all _ I _ put you through
You were tryin' to tell _ me _ all a - long _

al - ways tak - ing you for
some-thing in _ the love was

grant - ed.
miss - ing.

I nev - er saw it from your _ point of view _
You said it's not too late _ to _ get it back _

blind - ed by _ the doub - le stan - dards.
but I just _ was - n't

list'n - ing.

If I knew back then _ what I know now, _

if I un - der-stood _ the what, when,

why and how, _

now it's clear to me _

what I should have done, _

but

hind - sight _ is twen - ty twen - ty,

twen - ty twen - ty

vi - sion. _

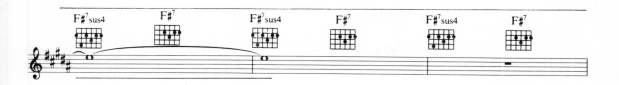

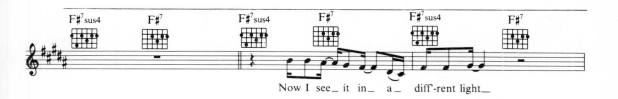

Now I see _ it in _ a _ diff-rent light _

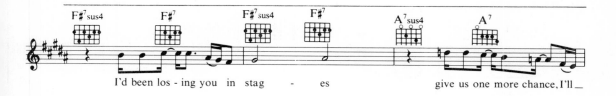

I'd been los - ing you in stag - es   give us one more chance, I'll _

get it right, _   girl, you're gon-na see _ some chang - es

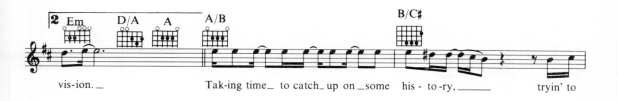

vis-ion. _   Tak-ing time _ to catch _ up on _ some his - to-ry, _____   tryin' to

fig-ure out ___ what went wrong with you and me. _   And it does-n't real - ly mat-ter what's

been be-fore,___ but I know there's no fut - ure with you wal-kin' out that door.___

If I knew back then___ what I know now,___ if I

un - der-stood___ the what, when, why and how,___ now it's clear to me _____ what I

should have done,___ but hind - sight___ is twen-ty twen-ty vi - sion.___

93
Uptown Girl

Words & Music by Billy Joel

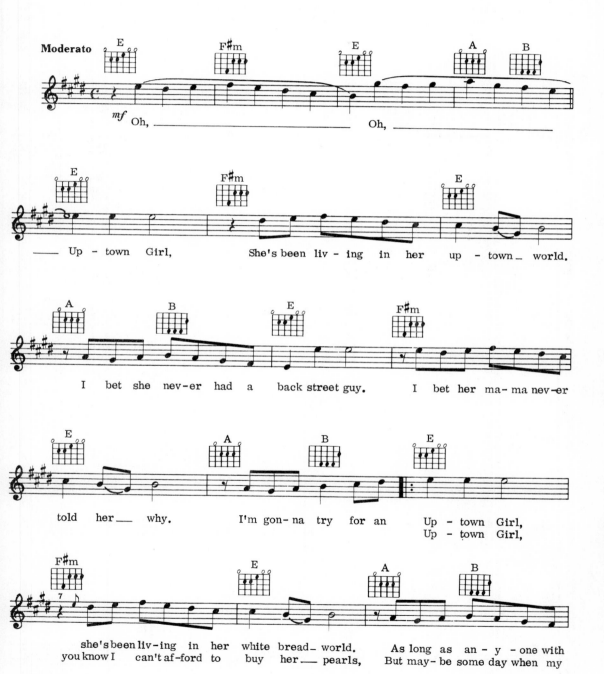

Moderato

mf Oh, _____ Oh, _____

__ Up - town Girl, She's been liv - ing in her up - town __ world.

I bet she nev - er had a back street guy. I bet her ma - ma nev - er

told her __ why. I'm gon - na try for an Up - town Girl,
Up - town Girl,

she's been liv - ing in her white bread __ world. As long as an - y - one with
you know I can't af - ford to buy her __ pearls, But may - be some day when my

hot blood can, ____ And now she's look- ing for a down – town __ man,
ship comes in, ____ she'll un – der – stand what kind of guy I've__ been,

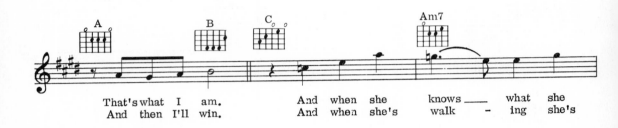

That's what I am. And when she knows ____ what she
And then I'll win. And when she's walk – ing she's

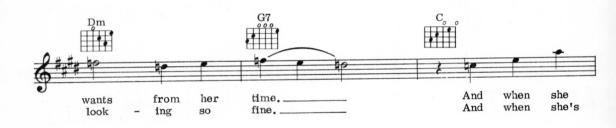

wants from her time. ____ And when she
look – ing so fine. ____ And when she's

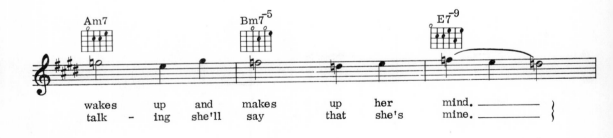

wakes up and makes up her mind. ____
talk – ing she'll say that she's mine. ____

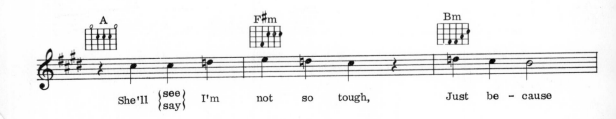

She'll {see} {say} I'm not so tough, Just be – cause

I'm in love with an Up - town Girl,
{You know I've seen her in her
{she's been liv -ing in her

up - town_ world. She's get - ting ti - red of her high class toys, ___
white bread_ world, As long as an - y - one with hot blood can, ___

And all her pre-sents from her up - town_ boys, She's got a choice.
And now she's look-ing for a down-town_ man, That's what I am.

Oh, _____

Oh, _____

Up -town Girl, _ 1. {She's my} Up - town Girl, ___ Don't you know I'm in love with an
                     {My   }

Repeat to fade

94
Union Of The Snake

Words & Music by Duran Duran

95
Vienna

Words & Music by M. Ure, B. Currie, W. Cann & C. Cross

Moderately

We walked in the cold ___ air, ___
mu - sic is weav - ing ___

freez - ing breath on the win-dow pane, ly - ing and wait - ing. ___
haunt-ing notes pizz - i - ca - to strings, the rhy -thm is call - ing. ___

A man in the dark in the pic - ture frame so
A - lone in the night as the day-light brings a

mys - tic and soul - ful. ___
cold emp-ty si - lence. ___

The
A

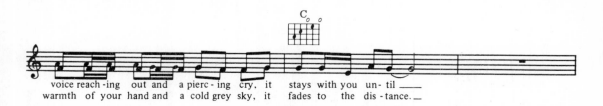

voice reach-ing out and a pierc-ing cry, it stays with you un - til ___
warmth of your hand and a cold grey sky, it fades to the dis-tance. ___

The feel-ing is gone, on-ly you and I, this means no-thing to me,
The im-age is gone, on-ly you and I, this means no-thing to me,

This means no-thing to me. _____
This means no-thing to me. _____ Oh ___ Vi-en-na _____

al Coda

Instr.

1.

2.

D.%. al Coda

The

This means

CODA

96
Waiting In Vain

Words & Music by Bob Marley

So don't___ treat me like a pup-pet on a string___
In life I know there's lots of grief

'Cos I know how to do my
But your love is my re -

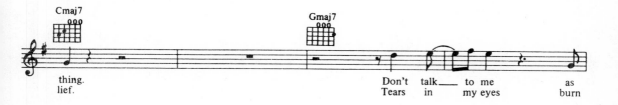

thing.
lief.
Don't talk___ to me as
Tears in my eyes as burn

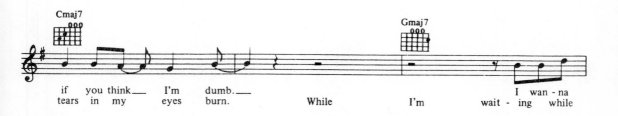

if you think___ I'm dumb.___
tears in my eyes burn.
While I'm wait - ing while

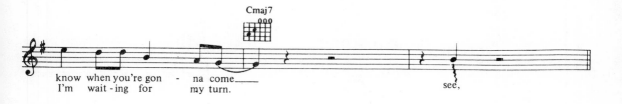

know when you're gon - na come.___ I wan - na
I'm wait - ing for my turn. see,

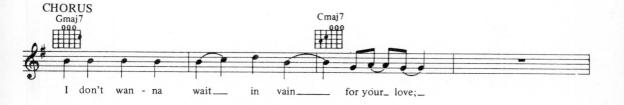

CHORUS

I don't wan - na wait___ in vain___ for your_ love;___

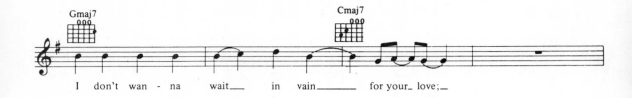

I don't wan - na wait___ in vain___ for your_ love;___

To Coda ⊕

I don't wan - na wait___ in vain___ for your_ love.___

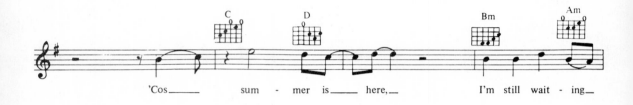

'Cos___ sum - mer is___ here,___ I'm still wait - ing___

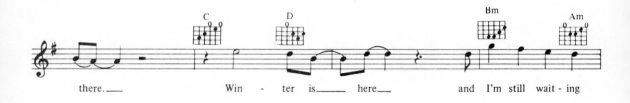

there.___ Win - ter is___ here___ and I'm still wait - ing

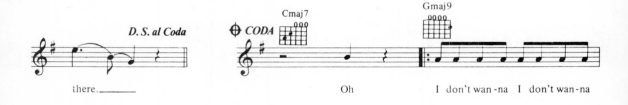

D. S. al Coda   ⊕ *CODA*

there.___   Oh   I don't wan - na I don't wan - na

Repeat to fade

I don't wan - na I don't wan - na I don't wan - na wait in vain.___   No___

97
We Close Our Eyes

Words & Music by Peter Cox & Richard Drummie

In - side ___ ev - 'ry-one hides one ___ de-sire

out - side, ___ no one would know. ___

Dan - ger, ___ close to the edge of ___ the knife
No show, ___ Wednes-day girl waits with the wine.
Her - oes, ___ ne - ver give in to ___ the night.

saf - er not to let go ___ and while we ___
she knows just what to say ___ while ___ no ___
he knows how far he can run ___ and as he ___

98
We Don't Need Another Hero

Words & Music by Graham Lyle & Terry Britten

VERSE 2:

Looking for something we can rely on,
There's got to be something better out there.
Love and compassion, their day is coming,
All else are castles built in the air.

99
Why Can't We Live Together

Words & Music by Timmy Thomas

why.
wars.
col - our ___

Gm7

Um, _____ Why can't we live to-
Um, Just a lit - tle peace in this
Um, _____ You are still my

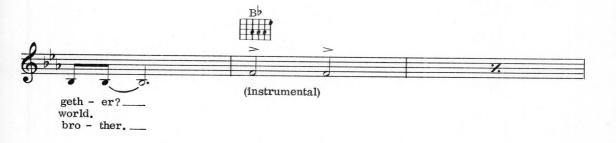

Bb

geth - er? ___
world.
bro - ther. ___

(instrumental)

Ev - 'ry - bo - dy wants to live to - geth - er; why

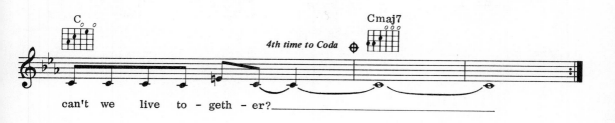

C

4th time to Coda

Cmaj7

can't we live to - geth - er? _____

CODA Cm6

C7

Live to - geth - er.

repeat and fade

100
Yah Mo B There

Words & Music by
James Ingram, Michael McDonald, Rod Temperton & Quincy Jones

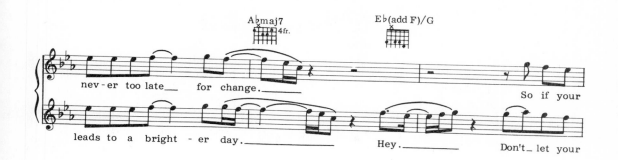

nev-er too late___ for change.___   So if your

leads to a bright - er day.___   Hey.___   Don't_ let your

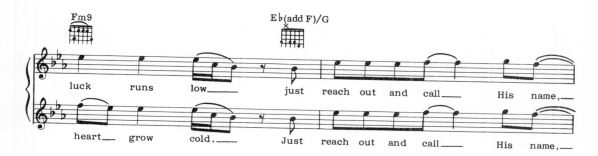

luck runs low___   just reach out and call___ His name,___

heart__ grow cold.___   Just reach out and call___ His name,___

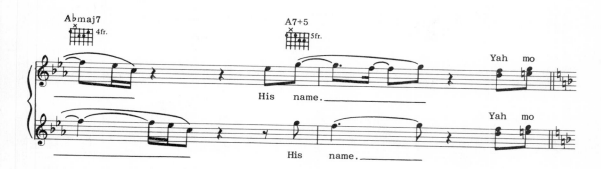

Yah mo

His name.___   Yah mo

His name.___

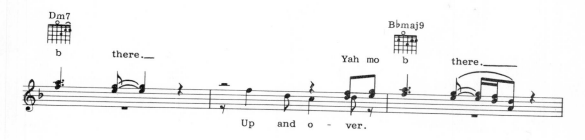

b   there.__   Yah mo b   there.___

Up and o - ver.

Yah mo b   there.__   Yah mo

Up and o - ver.__   Up and o - ver.

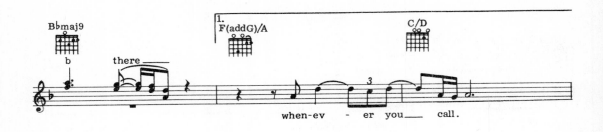

Bbmaj9 ... there ... / **1. F(addG)/A** ... when-ev - er you__ call. / **C/D**

No chord

2. F(addG)/A Yah mo b there.__ / Up and o - ver.__ **Cm7/F** You can count on it, broth - er,__ 'cause we're all__ **Gm9** 3fr.

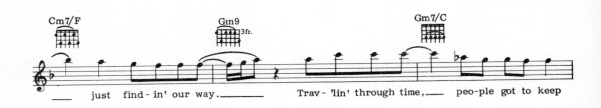

Cm7/F __ just find - in' our way.___ **Gm9** 3fr. Trav - 'lin' through time,__ peo-ple got to keep **Gm7/C**

Dm7 push-in' on__ no mat-ter how__ **Gm7** 3fr. man-y dreams slip a - way. **A7+5** 5fr. Yah mo__ b__ there.__

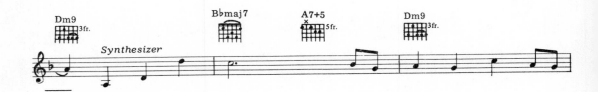

Dm9 3fr. *Synthesizer* **Bbmaj7** **A7+5** 5fr. **Dm9** 3fr.

Well, it's a dog - gone shame__ but nev-er too late   for change.__

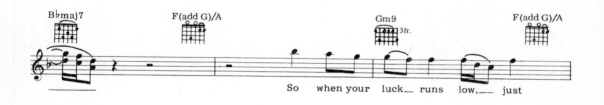

So   when your   luck__ runs   low,__   just

reach out and call__ His   name._____   Just call   His   name._____

Repeat and fade

b   there.__   Yah mo   b   there.__   Yah mo

Up   and o - ver.   Up   and o - ver.__

101
When You're Young And In Love

Words & Music by Van McCoy